A Giant in the Forest

Illustrated by Kellie Lewis

CELEBRATION PRESS
Pearson Learning Group

Once upon a time there was a little boy
who lived next to a cool, green forest.
There was a lake in the forest.

A big, ugly giant lived in the forest. The
giant liked to sleep all day. But at night
he walked in the forest, looking for things
to eat.

Every week the little boy's mother gave him a big bar of soap. Then she sent him to the lake to take a bath.

"You'll be safe in the lake because the giant can't swim," she always said. "But don't forget to be home before dark."

One day when the little boy was going to take his bath, he saw a baby bird on the ground. It had fallen out of its nest.
The boy put the bird back in its nest. ✱

The mother bird was so happy that she sang a song. It was a pretty song, and the boy sat down to listen.

The little boy stayed too long. It was getting dark when he got to the lake. He took his bath as fast as he could. Then he started home.

He hadn't gone far when he saw a huge footprint on the ground.

Then he saw something else. It was the big, ugly giant!

The little boy turned and ran back to the lake. The big giant was right behind him.

The little boy dropped his bar of soap on
the ground right in front of the giant.
The giant stepped on the soap and slipped.
He fell into the lake. SPLASH!

That's how the little boy saved
himself from the big giant who walked
in the cool, green forest at night.